The Little Prince

AS IMAGINED BY
OLIVIER SUPIOT

Editing and production: *Ediciones San Marcos S. L. –* Madrid

Text: *Ediciones San Marcos*
Photographs: *G. M. Azumendi, A. Vázquez* and *E. López-Tapia*
Production: *Diego Blas, Luis Blas, Teresa Solana*
English translation: *Lesley Ashcroft*
Design: *Alberto Caffaratto*

Printing and binding: *Jomagar,* Madrid

I.S.B.N.: 978-9962-8805-5-4
Legal Deposit: M-6313-2007

My dear Rose,

Even though it was under difficult circumstances, I'm so happy to have seen you on the planet of the Astronomer. Am I being selfish? Because of me, you were placed in danger. I realized that we never know how much we care about others until we're in danger of losing them. I don't know what I'd do without you and Fox. Deep in my heart, I know that the Snake will one day try to use my fear of losing you, just as he has done with the fears of all his victims. How will I react? How could I choose between the well-being of an entire planet and my friends? Is this what it's like to be a grown-up, having to make impossible choices? When I think about you, I hope that I'll always find the strength to stay on the right path.

Right now, a dark planet looms in our path...with a little spot of bright light.

Are the inhabitants fighting off the Snake's shadows?

The Little Prince

First American edition published in 2013 by Graphic Universe™.

Le Petit Prince™

based on the masterpiece by Antoine de Saint-Exupéry

© 2013 LPPM

An animated series based on the novel *Le Petit Prince* by Antoine de Saint-Exupéry
Developed for television by Matthieu Delaporte, Alexandre de la Patellière, and Bertrand Gatignol
Directed by Pierre-Alain Chartier

© 2013 ÉDITIONS GLÉNAT
Copyright © 2013 by Lerner Publishing Group, Inc., for the current edition

Graphic Universe™
A division of Lerner Publishing Group, Inc.
241 First Avenue North
Minneapolis, MN 55401 U.S.A.

Website address: www.lernerbooks.com

Library of Congress Cataloging-in-Publication Data

Gonnard, Christel.
   [Planète des Globus. English]
   The planet of the night globes / story by Christel Gonnard ; design and illustrations by Élyum Studio ; adaptation by Guillaume Dorison ; translation, Carol Klio Burrell. — 1st American ed.
      p. cm. — (The little prince ; #06)
   ISBN 978-0-7613-8756-5 (lib. bdg. : alk. paper)
   1. Graphic novels. I. Dorison, Guillaume. II. Burrell, Carol Klio. III. Saint-Exupéry, Antoine de, 1900-1944. Petit prince. IV. Élyum Studio. V. Petit Prince (Television program) VI. Title.
PZ7.7.G655Pl 2013
741.5'944—dc23   2012028621

Manufactured in the United States of America
1 — DP — 12/31/12

THE NEW ADVENTURES
BASED ON THE MASTERPIECE BY ANTOINE DE SAINT-EXUPÉRY

The Little Prince

THE PLANET OF THE NIGHT GLOBES

Based on the animated series and an original story by Christel Gonnard

Design: Élyum Studio
Story: Guillaume Dorison
Artistic Direction: Didier Poli
Art: Diane Fayolle
Backgrounds: Jérôme Benoit & Isa Python
Coloring: Karine Lambin
Coloring (Flats): Jackyung Kim
Editing: Hong Kim-Seang
Editorial Consultant: Didier Convard

Translation: Carol Burrell

Graphic Universe™ • Minneapolis • New York

⭐ THE LITTLE PRINCE

The Little Prince has extraordinary gifts. His sense of wonder allows him to discover what no one else can see. The Little Prince can communicate with all the beings in the universe, even the animals and plants. His powers grow over the course of his adventures.

The Prince's uniform:
When he transforms into the uniform of a prince, he is more agile and quick. When faced with difficult situations, the Little Prince also uses a sword that lets him sketch and bring to life anything from his imagination.

His sketchbook:
When he is not in his Prince's clothing, the Little Prince carries a sketchbook. When he blows on the pages, they take wing and form objects that he'll find very useful. Like his sword, it's powered by stardust collected on his travels.

⭐ FOX

A grouch, a trickster, and, so he says, interested only in his next meal, Fox is in reality the Little Prince's best friend. As such, he is always there to give him help but also just as much to help him to grow and to learn about the world.

⭐ THE SNAKE

Even though the Little Prince still does not know exactly why, there can be no doubt that the Snake has set his mind to plunging the entire universe into darkness! And to accomplish his goal, this malicious being is ready to use any form of deception. However, the Snake never takes action himself. He prefers to bring out the wickedness in those beings he has chosen to bite, tempting them to put their own worlds in danger.

⭐ THE GLOOMIES

When people who have been "bitten" by the Snake have completely destroyed their own planets, they become Gloomies, slaves to their Snake master. The Gloomies act as a group and carry out the Snake's most vile orders so he can get the better of the Little Prince!

4

11

LAUDION, A SIMPLE LAMP SALESMAN, AND A BIT OF A COWARD, LEAPT AT THE CHANCE TO REMIND US ALL ABOUT THE OLD MYTH THAT THE GLOBES TURNED PEOPLE TO STONE.

HE SAID THAT THE FOREST WASN'T SAFE ANYMORE, AND EVEN WORSE, HE CLAIMED THAT THE GLOBES WERE GOING TO COME AND DESTROY US TO GET THE NECTAR THEY CRAVED. FEAR GRIPPED THE TOWN.

ACCORDING TO HIM, THERE WAS ONLY ONE SOLUTION: ALWAYS KEEP THE TOWN LIT UP. THE GLOBES HATE LIGHT--SUCH AS THE VERY LAMPS THAT LAUDION JUST HAPPENED TO BE SELLING.

THAT SCOUNDREL TOOK ADVANTAGE OF MY FRIEND FELINA'S MISFORTUNE AND THE GULLIBILITY OF THE TOWNSFOLK, JUST TO MAKE MONEY! BUT HE DIDN'T FOOL ME. I KNOW THAT THE GLOBES ARE PEACEFUL.

BUT THE GLOBES ATTACKED US WHILE WE WERE IN THE FOREST... MAYBE IT WAS BECAUSE OF THE LANTERN FOX WAS WEARING.

DON'T WORRY, FOVEA. FOX AND I WILL DO EVERYTHING IN OUR POWER TO SHED SOME LIGHT ON THIS MYSTERY!

MAMA, CAN SCRAPPY SLEEP WITH ME?

IF FOX DOESN'T MIND, FELIX!

HOW COULD I SAY NO? GRUMBLE MMRF...

I'M SO HAPPY TO HAVE FELIX. HE'S TRULY MY ONE TRUE LIGHT IN THESE DARK TIMES.

FOX!

FELIX! FERDINAND!

HMPH...I'M SURE THEY'RE AROUND HERE SOMEWHERE!

LOOK OUT, LITTLE PRINCE! BEHIND YOU!

FOVEA, GET OUT OF HERE!

OH, NOOO!

THIS IS A FINE OUTCOME, MASTER...HSSS... THE LAST DEFENDER OF DARKNESS HAS FALLEN...

NOW NOTHING CAN STOP THE VICTORY OF LIGHT!

STAY CALM! THEY'RE NOT DANGEROUS.

WE'LL NEVER PUT OUT ALL THESE AWFUL STREETLAMPS IN TIME!

46

SNIF...I'M GOING TO MISS FOX!

YOU WERE A REAL HERO ON THAT PLANET. IT TOOK COURAGE TO BE BRAVE WHEN YOU WERE SO SCARED, FOX.

YEP! I'M A HERO! CROSS ME AT YOUR PERIL!

THE END

ON PLANET RAINBOW, THERE ARE RED CAVES SO BEAUTIFUL THEY LOOK LIKE CASTLES!

THERE ARE TREES SO HUGE THEY HUG THE MOON.

THERE'S A RIVER THAT WINDS THROUGH A MAJESTIC FOREST LIKE A HUGE YELLOW SNAKE!

THE SEAS ARE COBALT BLUE. BIG AND LITTLE BEASTIES CRUISE IN A BALLET OF BUBBLES.

?

TRANSLATION BY CAROL BURRELL
WITH EXTRA PUNS DREAMED UP BY ANNE AND OWEN SMIT

Antoine de Saint-Exupéry, author of the novel *The Little Prince* on which these new adventures are based, was born on June 29, 1900, in Lyon, France. He was the third of five children: Marie-Madeleine, Simone, Antoine, François, and Gabrielle. It was when he was twelve years old, during his summer break from boarding school, that airplanes and flying first made a huge impression on him.

In 1920, he was accepted into the École des Beaux-Arts in Paris to study architecture, but the next year he joined the Second Aviation Regiment of the armed forces and received his pilot's license. In 1922, he had his first plane crash and suffered a head fracture. He had to leave the armed forces and work at different jobs on the ground to earn a living.

By May of 1926, Saint-Exupéry was able to fly again. He delivered airmail, which was a new and sometimes dangerous profession, on routes from France to Senegal and all the way to South America. That was where, in 1931, he met and married Consuelo Suncin.

From 1933 to 1938, Saint-Exupéry was very busy. He traveled to North Africa and Indochina and attempted to break the flight speed record from Paris to Saigon, Vietnam—during which his plane crashed again. It went down in the middle of the Sahara Desert. After his recovery, his life became even busier. He wrote newspaper reports in Spain on the Spanish Civil War, scouted airplane routes between Casablanca and Timbuktu, wrote a screenplay, registered several patents, and traveled to the United States. In 1939, with the start of World War II, he returned to France and talked his way into a job as a high-risk reconnaissance pilot for the French Air Force. But this only lasted until France reached an armistice agreement with Germany.

In December 1940, Saint-Exupéry returned to visit friends in New York, where he finally began work on *The Little Prince*. The story is narrated by a pilot who has crashed his plane into the Sahara Desert. He meets a little prince visiting from a faraway asteroid. Along the way, the prince also meets Fox and Snake. By late 1942, after spending the spring and summer writing and illustrating, Saint-Exupéry had completed his novel, and in April 1943 it was published in his native language of French *(Le Petit Prince)* and in English.

Saint-Exupéry was eager to return to the war. He decided to join the Free French Forces in Algeria, who were continuing the fight against the Axis powers. Because of his age, at first he had a hard time convincing them to let him fly. He was authorized to fly five dangerous missions. In fact, he flew eight. On July 31, 1944, Saint-Exupéry went on a scouting flight to prepare for military landings in the south of France. His plane disappeared over the water, and he was never seen again.

Over the decades since *The Little Prince* was published, it has gone on to become one of the best-selling novels of all time. In 2003, a small moon in our solar system's asteroid belt was named Petit-Prince in honor of the masterpiece Saint-Exupéry created.

THE LITTLE PRINCE IN THE TWENTY-FIRST CENTURY

The Little Prince is a landmark of literature and one of the most translated and beloved books in the world. It tackles universal topics with a unique philosophical and poetic sensibility. Sixty-five years after the first edition, the Saint-Exupéry Estate decided to bring the character back for a whole new generation . . . and for everyone who has ever loved the boy who sees the world with his heart.

The Little Prince now returns in a series of new adventures that remain true to the spirit of the original work. He will travel from planet to planet chasing the wicked Snake, who wants to plunge the whole universe into darkness. On each planet, the Snake sends bad thoughts into the minds of its inhabitants, making them sad and grim, draining the life out of their planet. The Little Prince must leave his beautiful Rose behind and must use his vision and courage to defeat the Snake, bringing along his friend Fox to save planets in danger across the universe.

ABOUT THE ADAPTERS

After several years in video games and Japanese animation, adapter Guillaume Dorison became literary editor for the publisher Les Humanoïdes Associés in 2006, where he launched the Shogun Collection dedicated to original manga. In June 2010, he founded Élyum Studio with Didier Poli, Jean-Baptiste Hostache, and Xavier Dorison to provide services for the creation of graphic novels. In addition to his position as director of writing for Élyum Studio, he has more than two dozen comics and manga to his credit under the pseudonym IZU, has written several titles in the Explora series on world explorers for French publisher Glénat, and won the 2010 Animeland Prize for best French manga.

Didier Poli, artistic director for the new graphic novel adaptations based on *The Little Prince*, was born in Lyon in 1971. After graduate studies in applied arts, he worked for various animation studios including Disney. He was working as artistic director for the video game company Kalisto Entertainment when he met Manuel Bichebois in 2001 and began drawing Bichebois's graphic novel series L'Enfant de l'orage. At the 2004 Nîmes Festival, Didier Poli received the Bronze Boar prize for young talent. He continues, along with his work on graphic novels, to work regularly in cartoons and video games as a designer and storyboard artist.